W9-CJF-531

## The route to your roots
### Founder Editors: Anant Pai

When they look back at their formative years, many Indians nostalgically recall the vital part Amar Chitra Katha picture books have played in their lives. It was **ACK – Amar Chitra Katha** – that first gave them a glimpse of their glorious heritage.

Since they were introduced in 1967, there are now **over 400 Amar Chitra Katha** titles to choose from. **Over 100 million copies** have been sold worldwide.

Now the Amar Chitra Katha titles are even more widely available in **1000+ bookstores all across India**. Log on to www.ack-media.com to locate a bookstore near you. If you do not have access to a bookstore, you can buy all the titles through our online store **www.amarchitrakatha.com**. We provide quick delivery anywhere in the world.

To make it easy for you to locate the titles of your choice from our treasure trove of titles, the books are now arranged in six categories.

### Epics and Mythology
Best known stories from the Epics and the Puranas

### Indian Classics
Enchanting tales from Indian literature

### Fables and Humour
Evergreen folktales, legends and tales of wisdom and humour

### Bravehearts
Stirring tales of brave men and women of India

### Visionaries
Inspiring tales of thinkers, social reformers and nation builders

### Contemporary Classics
The Best of Modern Indian literature

## Amar Chitra Katha Pvt Ltd

© Amar Chitra Katha Pvt Ltd, August 2016, Reprinted February 2017,
ISBN 978-93-8587-469-7
Published by Amar Chitra Katha Pvt. Ltd., 201 & 202, Sumer Plaza,
2nd Floor, Marol Maroshi Road, Andheri (East), Mumbai- 400 059. India
Printed at M/s Indigo press (I) Pvt Ltd., Mumbai.
For Consumer Complaints Contact Tel : +91-22 49188881/82/83
Email: customerservice@ack-media.com

# KRISHNA
## The Protector of Dharma

# Contents

**Colourists:** C. Ramesh and Adarsh Achari

**Special Pages**
**Text:** Editorial
**Art:** Ritoparna Hazra
**Design:** Bidya Pradhan

**Cover:** Yusuf Bangalorewala

**Art Director:** Savio Mascarenhas
**Executive Editor:** Reena I. Puri

# KRISHNA

VASUDEVA, A NOBLEMAN, HAD MARRIED PRINCESS DEVAKI OF MATHURA. HE WAS TAKING HIS BRIDE HOME.

DEVAKI'S COUSIN, PRINCE KAMSA, WAS DRIVING THE CHARIOT. HE WAS CRUEL AND THE PEOPLE FEARED HIM.

IT'S KAMSA! RUN!

HA! LOOK AT THEM RUN, VASUDEVA!

JUST THEN A HEAVENLY VOICE WAS HEARD.

KAMSA, YOU SHALL SOON DIE. THE EIGHTH CHILD BORN TO DEVAKI WILL SLAY YOU!

IF SHE LIVES TO HAVE THAT EIGHTH CHILD! I'LL SLAY HER BEFORE, THEN!

KAMSA, DON'T!

YOUR SISTER HAS DONE YOU NO HARM, KAMSA. AS FOR THE CHILDREN WHO ARE YET TO BE BORN, I SHALL GIVE EACH ONE TO YOU, THE MOMENT IT IS BORN. I PROMISE.

I'LL SPARE DEVAKI, BUT I'LL MAKE SURE THAT YOU KEEP YOUR WORD.

KAMSA CONFINED DEVAKI AND VASUDEVA IN A PALACE. HE VISITED THEM EVERY TIME A BABY WAS BORN.

DEVAKI, GIVE ME THE BABY.

NO!

STOP HIM, MY LORD!

I AM HELPLESS, DEVAKI!

THUS DID THE COUPLE LOSE SIX OF THEIR CHILDREN. WHEN THE SEVENTH ONE WAS ABOUT TO BE BORN—

WE MUST TRY AND SAVE THIS CHILD, DEVAKI.

FROM THAT TYRANT, KAMSA? WE WILL NEVER SUCCEED.

WHO WILL HELP US? WHO WILL DARE RAISE A FINGER AGAINST ONE WHO HAS IMPRISONED HIS OWN FATHER?

YES. KING UGRASENA'S PLIGHT IS NO BETTER THAN OURS.

BUT DON'T LOSE HEART. REMEMBER THE PROPHECY.

THE SEVENTH CHILD WAS MIRACULOUSLY CARRIED TO ROHINI, VASUDEVA'S SECOND WIFE, IN GOKUL.

AND KAMSA WAS TOLD THAT DEVAKI'S BABY WAS STILL-BORN.

GOOD. THE NEXT WILL BE THE EIGHTH ONE — THE SLAYER OF MIGHTY KAMSA. HA!

PRADYOTA, HAVE VASUDEVA AND DEVAKI PUT IN CHAINS.

AS THE MONTHS WENT BY, HOWEVER, KAMSA GREW RESTLESS. CHANURA, THE COURT WRESTLER SENSED THIS.

LORD, WHY DON'T YOU COME TO THE GYMNASIUM?

NO, CHANURA!

I'LL BE AT PEACE ONLY WHEN I'VE KILLED THE EIGHTH CHILD.

IT RAINED HEAVILY ON THE EIGHTH DAY OF THE WANING MOON OF SHRAVAN*.

LORD! I THINK THE TIME HAS COME.

THE EIGHTH CHILD!

IT WAS PAST MIDNIGHT WHEN THE CHILD WAS BORN.

WHAT A BEAUTIFUL BABY HE IS! AND HE KNOWS HE MUST NOT CRY!

*5TH MONTH OF THE HINDU CALENDAR. STARTS LATE JULY AND ENDS IN 3RD WEEK OF AUGUST.

HOW I LONG TO HOLD MY SON... BUT... THESE CHAINS...

SUDDENLY—

LOOK! THE CHAINS HAVE FALLEN OFF.

AND THE DOORS HAVE OPENED! IT'S A MIRACLE!

DEVAKI! QUICK! GIVE THE CHILD TO ME.

I'LL TAKE HIM TO OUR FRIEND, NANDA, IN GOKUL.

AND VASUDEVA WALKED PAST THE GUARDS WHO HAD FALLEN ASLEEP.

GOKUL WAS ON THE OPPOSITE BANK OF THE RIVER YAMUNA WHICH WAS THEN IN SPATE.

AS VASUDEVA APPROACHED, HOWEVER, THE WATERS PARTED...

... AND VASUDEVA WALKED TOWARDS GOKUL.

AS HE NEARED GOKUL —

AH! THE CRY OF A NEW-BORN BABY. IT COMES FROM NANDA'S HOUSE.

NANDA'S WIFE YASHODA HAS HAD A CHILD.

IT'S A GIRL!

AND SURELY KAMSA WOULD NOT KILL A BABY GIRL.

SO VASUDEVA LEFT HIS EIGHTH CHILD IN NANDA'S HOUSE AND CARRIED THE BABY GIRL TO MATHURA.

THE CHILD IS QUIET, AND THE GUARDS ARE STILL ASLEEP.

AS SOON AS VASUDEVA ENTERED THE PALACE, THE DOORS CLOSED. MINUTES LATER—

DID YOU HEAR THAT? IT'S THE WAIL OF A NEW-BORN BABY!

OOAH! OOAH!

COME! LET'S REPORT THIS TO THE KING!

THE EIGHTH CHILD! I WILL BE THERE IN A MOMENT.

WHEN KAMSA REACHED THE PALACE—

SPARE THE BABY, KAMSA. WHAT HARM CAN A GIRL DO YOU?

IGNORING HIM, KAMSA SEIZED THE BABY BY ITS LEGS AND WAS ABOUT TO DASH IT TO THE GROUND WHEN···

···IT ESCAPED FROM HIS GRIP AND FLEW TOWARDS THE SKY.

THEN—

THE ONE WHO SHALL DESTROY YOU STILL LIVES!

THE NEXT DAY, IN GOKUL—

THEY SAY THAT NANDA'S SON IS VERY BEAUTIFUL.

YES. AND HE HAS A BEAUTIFUL, NAME TOO— KRISHNA!

KAMSA SET DEVAKI AND VASUDEVA FREE. HOWEVER, HE WANTED TO TRACE THE EIGHTH CHILD. SO HE SENT FOR THE WICKED PUTANA.

PUTANA! GO OUT AND KILL EVERY CHILD BORN IN THE MONTH OF SHRAVAN!

PUTANA WENT ABOUT HER EVIL TASK.

I'LL SMEAR MY BREASTS WITH POISON AND FEED THE BABIES.

WHAT A SWEET BABY! MAY I HOLD IT?

THE MOTHER WAS FLATTERED. SHE GAVE THE BABY TO PUTANA.

A FEW MINUTES LATER—

MY BABY! WHAT'S HAPPENED TO MY BABY? AND WHERE IS PUTANA?

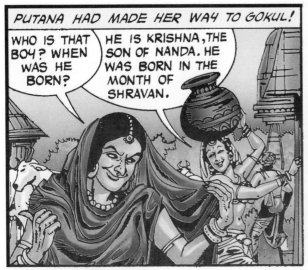

PUTANA HAD MADE HER WAY TO GOKUL!

WHO IS THAT BOY? WHEN WAS HE BORN?

HE IS KRISHNA, THE SON OF NANDA. HE WAS BORN IN THE MONTH OF SHRAVAN.

WHEN PUTANA FOUND KRISHNA ALONE—

LATER—

WHERE IS KRISHNA? I HAD LEFT HIM HERE!

OH! HE IS SAFE. BUT... WHO IS THIS WOMAN? WHY IS SHE LYING HERE?

I SAW HER NURSING KRISHNA.

THEN SHE MUST BE PUTANA! PUTANA THE BABY-KILLER. SHE HAS KILLED MANY BABIES IN MATHURA.

SHE IS DEAD! THE EVIL PUTANA IS DEAD!

KRISHNA WAS SAFE, AND LIFE IN GOKUL WENT ON AS BEFORE.

AS THE YEARS WENT BY, KRISHNA GREW TO BE AN ADORABLE LITTLE BOY.

KRISHNA! COME. I HAVE SOME FRESH BUTTER FOR YOU.

MAY I HAVE SOME MORE, MOTHER?

NO, KRISHNA. THAT'S ENOUGH FOR TODAY.

HERE'S BALARAMA*! GO AND PLAY WITH HIM.

THE TWO BOYS RAN OUT TO MEET THEIR FRIENDS.

KRISHNA, LET'S GO AND PLAY ON THE BANK OF THE YAMUNA.

WAIT. I'LL JOIN YOU IN A MINUTE.

KRISHNA TIPTOED INTO A NEARBY HOUSE...

...AND WENT STRAIGHT TO THE POTS OF BUTTER. SUDDENLY—

YOU NAUGHTY BOY! WHAT HAVE YOU DONE?

SHE DRAGGED KRISHNA TO YASHODA.

KRISHNA HAS EATEN ALL THE BUTTER IN MY HOUSE.

MY KRISHNA DID THAT? I DON'T BELIEVE IT. WHY, I GAVE HIM A WHOLE POT OF BUTTER ONLY A SHORT WHILE AGO.

BUT...

SISTER, YOU MUST KEEP THE MILK AND BUTTER BEYOND THE REACH OF CHILDREN.

THE GOPIKAS, AS THE WOMEN OF GOKUL WERE CALLED, TOOK YASHODA'S ADVICE. BUT KRISHNA WAS TOO CLEVER FOR THEM.

WHAT SHALL WE DO?

I HAVE AN IDEA.

SUCH WERE THE PRANKS KRISHNA PLAYED AND YASHODA FOUND IT DIFFICULT TO HANDLE THE COMPLAINTS THAT POURED IN.

YASHODA! KRISHNA WAS DRINKING THE MILK STRAIGHT FROM MY COW!

BUT MOTHER, THE COW GAVE IT TO ME.

AND THE BUTTER ON YOUR FACE? WHO GAVE THAT TO YOU?

THE GWALA BOYS SMEARED IT ON MY FACE. ALL OUT OF SPITE.

LOOK, MOTHER! I AM SO SHORT. THE BUTTER POT IS KEPT SO HIGH. HOW COULD I REACH IT?

KRISHNA, YOU ARE BECOMING NAUGHTIER DAY BY DAY. I WILL HAVE TO PUNISH YOU!

SO SHE TIED KRISHNA TO A HEAVY MORTAR.

BALARAMA WILL UNTIE ME. I'LL GO TO HIM.

BUT WHILE HE WAS ON HIS WAY THE MORTAR WAS CAUGHT BETWEEN TWO TREES.

HE PULLED WITH ALL HIS HIS MIGHT TILL...

...THE TREES CRASHED TO THE GROUND.

AS THE NEWS SPREAD, A CROWD GATHERED AT THE SPOT.

THIS BOY IS A MARVEL!

HE UPROOTED THOSE TWO MIGHTY TREES!

THESE STRANGE HAPPENINGS FRIGHTENED THE PEOPLE. SO THEY DECIDED TO LEAVE GOKUL AND GO TO VRINDAVAN.

AT VRINDAVAN —

MOTHER, MAY I GO WITH THE OTHERS TO GRAZE THE CATTLE?

YOU MAY, IF YOU STAY BY BALARAMA'S SIDE.

IN THE EVENING —

KRISHNA, WE ARE TOO TIRED TO HERD THE CATTLE.

WELL, THEN, I'LL HERD THEM FROM HERE.

KRISHNA TOOK UP HIS FLUTE.

SUCH SWEET MUSIC!

LOOK AT THE COWS!

THE GOPIKAS STOPPED THEIR CHORES TO LISTEN TO THE MELODIOUS STRAINS OF KRISHNA'S FLUTE.

HIS MUSIC FILLS ME WITH A STRANGE YEARNING.

ONE DAY —

IT'S HASTIN! RUN, KRISHNA!

I WON'T, I'LL TAME HIM.

PLEASE COME BACK, KRISHNA! HE'LL HURT YOU.

AS KRISHNA NEARED HIM, THE BULL SNORTED FIERCELY AND CHARGED.

BUT KRISHNA WAS TOO QUICK FOR HIM.

QUIET, MY FRIEND. I WON'T HURT YOU.

THUS DID KRISHNA, FIRMLY BUT GENTLY CALM THE ANGRY BULL.

ONE DAY KRISHNA FOUND ONE OF HIS FRIENDS CRYING.

WHAT'S THE MATTER? WHY ARE YOU CRYING?

MY COWS ARE DEAD. THEY DRANK WATER FROM KALIYA'S POOL.

...ONLY TO FIND KRISHNA DANCING ON THE HOOD OF A MEEK KALIYA.

WHAT A BOY!

KRISHNA ORDERED KALIYA TO LEAVE THE POOL WITH HIS FAMILY. PEACE RETURNED TO VRINDAVAN.

ONE DAY, AS THE PEOPLE OF VRINDAVAN WERE PREPARING TO WORSHIP INDRA —

WE WORSHIP INDRA BECAUSE WE ARE AFRAID OF HIM WE OUGHT TO WORSHIP MOUNT GOVARDHANA WHOM WE LOVE!

KRISHNA IS RIGHT.

BUT WHILE GOVARDHANA WAS BEING WORSHIPPED, LOUD CLAPS OF THUNDER WERE HEARD...

...AND IT STARTED RAINING HEAVILY.

INDRA IS ANGRY. WE SHOULDN'T HAVE WORSHIPPED GOVARDHANA.

WHEN NEWS OF KRISHNA'S DEEDS REACHED MATHURA—

PRADYOTA! I HEAR THAT KRISHNA HELD THE MIGHTY GOVARDHANA ON HIS LITTLE FINGER.

SO THEY SAY, MY LORD!

YOU FOOL! WHY HAVE YOU LET HIM LIVE SO LONG? DIDN'T I ORDER YOU TO HAVE HIM KILLED SOMEHOW?

I HAVE TRIED EVERYTHING. EVEN THE MAD BULL, ARISHTA, AND THE WILD HORSE, KESHI.

KAMSA WAS SILENT FOR A WHILE. THEN—

HAVE IT ANNOUNCED THAT IN A FORTNIGHT I WILL PERFORM THE BOW SACRIFICE···

···AND···INVITE ALL, INCLUDING KRISHNA. YOU MUST SEE TO IT THAT HE DOES NOT RETURN ALIVE.

WHEN PRADYOTA LEFT, KAMSA SENT FOR CHANURA.

CHANURA! IF KRISHNA IS NOT KILLED BY PRADYOTA, CHALLENGE HIM TO A MATCH AND DON'T LET HIM ESCAPE ALIVE.

HE ALSO SUMMONED THE CHIEF OF MAHOUTS.

YOU WILL STAND AT THE ENTRANCE TO THE YAGNA HALL. WHEN KRISHNA COMES THERE SEE THAT YOUR ELEPHANT TRAMPLES HIM TO DEATH.

THEN HE SENT FOR THE WISE AKRURA.

I WANT THE WHOLE WORLD TO KNOW OF KRISHNA. ASK HIM TO COME TO MATHURA, FOR THE BOW SACRIFICE.

AKRURA SET OUT ON HIS MISSION.

AT VRINDAVAN—

YOU MUST PERMIT KRISHNA TO COME TO MATHURA.

NO, AKRURA I DON'T TRUST KAMSA. I WILL NOT SEND MY SON.

WHEN AKRURA SAW THAT NANDA WAS ADAMANT, HE TOLD HIM THE TRUTH ABOUT KRISHNA.

NANDA! KRISHNA IS THE SON OF PRINCE VASUDEVA.

I DON'T BELIEVE IT.

SO AKRURA NARRATED THE STORY OF KRISHNA'S BIRTH AND HOW HE WAS BROUGHT TO GOKUL.

KRISHNA, DID YOU HEAR THAT? AKRURA SAYS THAT DEVAKI IS YOUR MOTHER. I AM YOUR MOTHER, AREN'T I?

PLEASE DON'T BE UPSET, MOTHER. I SHALL ALWAYS LOOK UPON YOU AS MY MOTHER. BUT...

...I SEEK THE PERMISSION OF MY ELDERS TO GO TO MATHURA!

VERY GOOD, MY BOY! THE YADAVA CHIEFS WILL SEE THAT NO HARM COMES TO YOU.

YOU MAY GO, MY SON. BUT BEWARE OF KAMSA.

THE NEXT MORNING, KRISHNA, ACCOMPANIED BY BALARAMA, LEFT FOR MATHURA.

TAKE CARE OF YOURSELVES, CHILDREN.

AND COME BACK SOON.

AS THEY NEARED THE CITY OF MATHURA, KRISHNA DECIDED TO WALK. SUDDENLY—

RISE, O WOMAN! WHY DO YOU FALL AT MY FEET?

LOOK AT TRIVAKRA! HER HUMPED BACK HAS STRAIGHTENED OUT.

A MIRACLE! HE MUST BE OUR SAVIOUR.

THE NEWS SPREAD AND A CROWD FOLLOWED KRISHNA AND BALARAMA TO THE GATE OF THE YAGNA HALL.

SIR, I AM KRISHNA. MAY I INSPECT THE BOW?

CERTAINLY! DO STEP IN.

IT WAS PRADYOTA.

SO THIS IS THE BOY I HAVE TO KILL.

IS THIS THE BOW? IT DOESN'T LOOK VERY HEAVY.

BUT IT IS! EVEN THE MIGHTY WRESTLER CHANURA CANNOT LIFT IT.

I STILL DON'T BELIEVE IT IS THAT HEAVY.

26

KRISHNA LIFTED THE BOW...

...AND BROKE IT.

THE JUBILANT CROWD RUSHED INTO THE SACRIFICIAL HALL.

VICTORY TO KRISHNA! HE IS THE SAVIOUR!

WHEN PRADYOTA WENT TO KAMSA WITH THE NEWS—

KRISHNA BROKE THE BOW AND YOU STOOD AND WATCHED HIM DO IT!

YOU HAD ORDERS TO KILL HIM, HADN'T YOU?

I KNOW, MY LORD! BUT THE CROWD THAT FOLLOWED HIM WAS FRIGHTENING.

THE NEXT MORNING AS KRISHNA APPROACHED THE GATE OF THE YAGNA HALL—

WATCH OUT, KRISHNA! THE ELEPHANT...!

THE ELEPHANT SEIZED KRISHNA.

BUT KRISHNA ESCAPED ITS GRIP, LIFTED IT BY ITS TRUNK...

...AND HURLING IT INTO THE AIR...

...KILLED IT.

THEN WITH BALARAMA, HE TOOK HIS PLACE IN THE ARENA WHERE THE GAMES WERE BEING HELD.

KRISHNA, KAMSA HAS HEARD MUCH ABOUT YOUR STRENGTH AND VALOUR. HE HAS INVITED YOU TO WRESTLE··· WITH ME!

IT'S AN HONOUR, CHANURA. I AM READY.

FIRST MUSHTIKA WILL WRESTLE WITH YOUR BROTHER.

BALARAMA AND MUSHTIKA FACED EACH OTHER.

IT IS UNFAIR OF KAMSA TO PIT THIS BOY AGAINST MUSHTIKA! HE'LL BE KILLED.

BUT THE CROWD WAS IN FOR A SURPRISE.

LOOK! MUSHTIKA IS IN TROUBLE!

IT WAS BALARAMA WHO KILLED MUSHTIKA.

NOW CHANURA STEPPED FORWARD.

ARE YOU READY, KRISHNA?

CHANURA TRIED TO CRUSH KRISHNA IN HIS MIGHTY ARMS. BUT KRISHNA SLIPPED AWAY.

DISAPPOINTED, CHANURA RUSHED MADLY AT HIM.

BUT KRISHNA NIMBLY STEPPED ASIDE AND PICKING HIM UP...

...DASHED HIM TO THE GROUND.

CHANURA IS DEAD!

VICTORY TO KRISHNA!

THUD

CRASH

AS KAMSA'S SOLDIERS MOVED TOWARDS THE YADAVA CHIEFS...

...KRISHNA RUSHED TOWARDS KAMSA...

...TOOK AWAY HIS SWORD...

...AND THROWING HIM TO THE GROUND, KILLED HIM.

THE CROWD WAS STUNNED INTO SILENCE. KRISHNA LIFTED THE CROWN FROM KAMSA'S HEAD...

# KRISHNA AND RUKMINI

RUKMI, THE SON OF KING BHEESHMAKA OF VIDARBHA, CAME HOME FROM MATHURA, BURSTING WITH NEWS.

AS THE MEMBERS OF THE ROYAL HOUSEHOLD SURROUNDED HIM —

KRISHNA, THE COWHERD FROM VRINDAVAN, HAS SLAIN KAMSA.

IT APPEARS THAT KRISHNA IS REALLY THE EIGHTH SON OF VASUDEVA AND DEVAKI, KAMSA'S COUSIN. HE AND HIS ELDER BROTHER, BALARAMA, WERE SECRETED AWAY TO GOKUL AS SOON AS THEY WERE BORN AND WERE BROUGHT UP AMONG THE COWHERDS.

SO IN SPITE OF ALL KAMSA'S EFFORTS THE PROPHECY HAS COME TRUE. IS KRISHNA REALLY A DIVINITY?

*RUKMI'S SISTER, RUKMINI, WAS A FORTHRIGHT GIRL.*

THEN HE IS NO COWHERD BUT A NOBLE YADAVA!

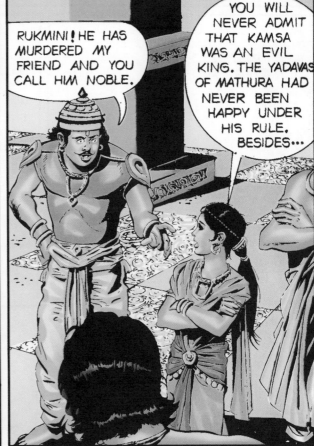

RUKMINI! HE HAS MURDERED MY FRIEND AND YOU CALL HIM NOBLE.

YOU WILL NEVER ADMIT THAT KAMSA WAS AN EVIL KING. THE YADAVAS OF MATHURA HAD NEVER BEEN HAPPY UNDER HIS RULE. BESIDES...

...DON'T FORGET HE DEPOSED HIS OWN FATHER AND USURPED THE THRONE.

I SUPPOSE KRISHNA WILL NOW BECOME THE KING.

NO! HE REFUSED THE CROWN. HE INSISTED THAT UGRASENA BE REINSTATED.

HE REFUSED THE CROWN!

YES! BUT KING UGRASENA AND THE NOBLES HAVE REQUESTED, NAY, INSISTED THAT HE REMAIN IN MATHURA AND···

WHO WOULDN'T! DID HE AGREE?

*RUKMI IGNORED HER AND CONTINUED TO SPEAK TO BHEESHMAKA.*

HE HAS AGREED TO STAY FOR A WHILE — TO LEARN THE SCRIPTURES AND THE PRINCELY ARTS.

WHAT ABOUT JARASANDHA? HOW DID HE REACT?

JARASANDHA, KAMSA'S FATHER-IN-LAW, WAS THE EMPEROR OF MAGADHA, THE MOST POWERFUL KINGDOM OF THOSE DAYS. MATHURA, LIKE VIDARBHA AND MOST OTHER KINGDOMS, OWED ALLEGIANCE TO HIM.

THE EMPEROR IS FURIOUS. BOTH HIS DAUGHTERS* HAVE BEEN WIDOWED IN ONE STROKE. HE VOWS TO TAKE REVENGE. HE HAS SENT FOR ME. I MUST GO AND SEE ABOUT THE CHARIOTS.

RUKMINI FOLLOWED HIM.

I MUST KNOW MORE ABOUT KRISHNA.

BHEESHMAKA AND HIS WIFE WERE ALONE.

THE BOY SEEMS TO BE VIRTUOUS. I CANNOT THINK OF A MORE SUITABLE HUSBAND FOR RUKMINI.

THE SAME THOUGHT OCCURRED TO ME. HE REFUSED THE CROWN OF MATHURA. HOW IT MUST HAVE PLEASED POOR, OLD UGRASENA.

AND MATTERS STOOD THERE.

*KAMSA'S WIVES

MEANWHILE, WITH THE HELP OF RUKMI AND OTHER ALLIES, JARASANDHA MADE SEVERAL ATTEMPTS TO AVENGE THE DEATH OF HIS SON-IN-LAW, BUT IN VAIN. AFTER THE EIGHTEENTH ATTEMPT—

THE VILE YADAVA AND HIS BROTHER HAVE DODGED US AGAIN. WE WILL HAVE TO BIDE OUR TIME. LET MY FRIENDS RETURN TO THEIR CAPITALS FOR THE PRESENT.

AT DWARAKA, KRISHNA'S INACCESSIBLE ISLAND CITY—

OUR SPIES SAY THAT JARASANDHA HAS DECIDED TO LIE LOW FOR A WHILE.

BALARAMA LOOKED AT KRISHNA WITH A MERRY TWINKLE IN HIS EYE.

NOW YOU'LL HAVE ALL THE LEISURE TO DREAM OF THE BEAUTIFUL PRINCESS OF VIDARBHA—THE MOST SOUGHT-AFTER PRINCESS ON EARTH.

AH, BALARAMA! MY MIND IS SET ON MARRYING HER. BUT HER FATHER IS A VASSAL OF JARASANDHA AND HER BROTHER, RUKMI, HIS STAUNCH ALLY.

BUT IT IS RUMOURED THAT BHEESHMAKA AND HIS WIFE SECRETLY HOPE THAT YOU WILL WIN RUKMINI.

MEANWHILE, AT VIDARBHA, IN THE GARDEN OF BHEESMAKA'S PALACE, RUKMINI TOO WAS LOST IN DREAMS OF THE YADAVA HERO WHO HAD WON HER HEART.

EVEN THE MIGHTY EMPEROR WITH ALL HIS ALLIES HAS NOT BEEN ABLE TO VANQUISH HIM. HE AND ONLY HE SHALL BE MY LORD.

SUDDENLY SHE HEARD VOICES.

MY FATHER! RUKMI! THEY'RE COMING THIS WAY.

THEY WERE DISCUSSING HER MARRIAGE.

YOUR MOTHER AND I HAVE DECIDED TO GIVE HER TO KRISHNA.

HOW FORTUNATE AM I!

HOW COULD YOU, FATHER? DON'T FORGET, HE MURDERED MY DEAR FRIEND, THE EMPEROR'S SON-IN-LAW. SURELY, WE CANNOT AFFORD TO DISPLEASE THE MIGHTY EMPEROR.

PLEASE RUKMI! DON'T MAKE HIM CHANGE HIS MIND!

BHEESHMAKA WAS SILENT FOR A WHILE. THEN—

BUT WE CANNOT THINK OF A MORE SUITABLE HUSBAND FOR HER. AFTER ALL JARASANDHA HAS NOT YET BEEN ABLE TO AVENGE KAMSA'S DEATH...

BUT HE CERTAINLY WILL. IT IS ONLY A MATTER OF TIME.

THEN WHOM DO YOU SUGGEST?

THE EMPEROR'S FAVOURITE AND MY FRIEND — SHISHUPALA, THE CROWN PRINCE OF CHEDI. HE IS ENAMOURED OF RUKMINI.

THAT JACKAL! NEVER! I SHALL NEVER MARRY HIM. O RUKMI, HOW COULD YOU SELL YOUR OWN SISTER TO WIN THE EMPEROR'S FAVOUR? DON'T AGREE, FATHER, PLEASE DON'T AGREE!

BUT BHEESHMAKA INVARIABLY PERMITTED HIS ELDEST SON TO MAKE ALL MAJOR DECISIONS, EVEN IF THEY DID NOT COINCIDE WITH HIS OWN WISHES. HE HEAVED A SIGH.

ALL RIGHT, RUKMI. DO AS YOU WILL.

THEN I SHALL SEND A FORMAL PROPOSAL TO CHEDI AND INVITE SHISHUPALA TO COME AND MARRY RUKMINI.

THEY WALKED AWAY, LITTLE KNOWING THAT RUKMINI HAD OVERHEARD EVERY WORD OF THEIR CONVERSATION.

SO THEY DON'T EVEN PLAN TO HOLD A SWAYAMWARA. TO WHOM SHALL I SPEAK? WHAT SHALL I DO?

SUDDENLY AN IDEA OCCURRED TO HER.

WHY NOT! WHY SHOULDN'T I? AFTER ALL MY PARENTS ARE FOR IT.

SHE WENT INTO THE PALACE AND SENT FOR SUNANDA—A BRAHMAN WHOM SHE TRUSTED AND WHO WAS DEVOTED TO HER. WHEN HE CAME—

WHY DO YOU LOOK SO PALE, MY LITTLE ONE? WHAT'S THE MATTER?

SHE TOLD HIM ABOUT THE CONVERSATION SHE HAD OVERHEARD. THEN—

O VENERABLE ONE, WOULD IT BE WRONG ON MY PART TO SEND A SECRET MESSAGE TO THE YADAVA HERO?

NO, LITTLE ONE, NEVER. IT WOULD BE WRONG TO MARRY SHISHU-PALA WHEN YOUR HEART IS SET ON ANOTHER AND YOUR PARENTS HAVE IN THEIR HEARTS APPROVED.

BUT WITH WHOM CAN I ENTRUST SUCH A MESSAGE?

I WILL GO TO DWARAKA, RUKMINI. I SHALL CARRY THE MESSAGE FOR YOU.

RUKMINI WROTE OUT THE MESSAGE AND...

...GAVE IT TO THE BRAHMAN, TELLING HIM WHAT HER PLANS WERE.

...AND BE SURE TO TELL HIM THAT I WOULD NOT WANT MY KITH AND KIN TO BE KILLED ON MY ACCOUNT.

DO NOT WORRY, RUKMINI. I WILL NOT FORGET.

WITH GREAT DIFFICULTY, SUNANDA REACHED DWARAKA WHERE HE WAS GIVEN A WARM WELCOME. AFTER HE WAS RESTED AND REFRESHED—

O VENERABLE ONE, IF IT WOULD NOT MEAN BETRAYING ANY CONFIDENCE, TELL US WHY YOU HAVE COME TO OUR INACCESSIBLE CITY?

I HAVE COME WITH A MESSAGE FROM RUKMINI, THE PRINCESS OF VIDARBHA.

RUKMINI! MY OWN RUKMINI!!

SUNANDA TOLD KRISHNA ABOUT THE CONVERSATION THAT RUKMINI HAD OVERHEARD. THEN HE GAVE KRISHNA, RUKMINI'S MESSAGE.

...I HAVE CHOSEN YOU AS MY HUSBAND. COME TO VIDARBHA, VANQUISH THE ARMIES OF JARASANDHA AND SHISHUPALA AND CLAIM ME...

WHEN KRISHNA FINISHED READING THE MESSAGE —

IF YOU DO NOT COME AND TAKE HER AWAY SHE HAS DECIDED TO GIVE UP HER LIFE.

SHE MENTIONS THAT IN THE MESSAGE. BUT LITTLE DOES SHE REALISE THAT I TOO HAVE SET MY HEART ON WINNING HER.

YES! I HAVE. BUT I KNOW THAT RUKMI DOES NOT WANT TO GIVE HER TO ME.

SUNANDA'S FACE FELL.

DOES THAT MEAN YOU WILL NOT...

NO. IT DOES NOT. NOW THAT SHE HAS REVEALED HER HEART TO ME, I SHALL MAKE HER MINE. I SHALL NOT HESITATE TO ROUT ALL THE KINGS WHO STAND IN MY WAY.

OVERJOYED, SUNANDA UNFOLDED THE REST OF RUKMINI'S PLANS. THEN —

THE GENTLE ONE IS ANXIOUS THAT THERE SHOULD BE NO FAMILY BLOOD SHED ON HER ACCOUNT.

IT IS BUT NATURAL FOR HER, A VERITABLE GODDESS,* TO FEEL THAT WAY.

* RUKMINI IS BELIEVED TO BE THE GODDESS LAXMI REBORN ON EARTH.

KRISHNA SENT FOR HIS CHARIOTEER. WHEN HE CAME —

GET MY CHARIOT READY AT ONCE, DARUKA. AND TELL BALARAMA THAT I SHALL BE LEAVING FOR VIDARBHA IMMEDIATELY.

MEANWHILE, RUKMI'S FORMAL PROPOSAL AND INVITATION HAD REACHED SHISHUPALA. HE WAS JUBILANT.

RUKMI SAYS THAT THERE IS NOT GOING TO BE ANY SWAYAM-WARA. ALL I HAVE TO DO IS TO GO TO VIDARBHA AND MARRY RUKMINI. THE EMPEROR MUST HEAR THE GOOD NEWS.

BUT JARASANDHA WAS NOT AS CONFIDENT.

IT'S NOT AS EASY AS YOU THINK. I DO NOT TRUST THAT VILE COWHERD. HE IS SURE TO HEAR OF THE NEWS AND SNATCH THE BRIDE AWAY. WE WILL HAVE TO BE PREPARED.

JARASANDHA SENT FOR ALL HIS VASSALS AND ALLIES.

I AM BENT ON SECURING THE PRINCESS OF VIDARBHA FOR SHISHUPALA. YOU MUST BE READY TO CONFRONT THE COWHERD IF HE COMES THERE AND TRIES TO TAKE AWAY THE BRIDE.

MEANWHILE, AS SOON AS KRISHNA HAD LEFT DWARAKA, ONE OF BALARAMA'S SPIES CAME TO HIM.

LORD, THE EMPEROR HAS INFORMED ALL HIS ALLIES TO MARCH TO VIDARBHA. HE EXPECTS TROUBLE FROM US.

AND KRISHNA HAS GONE ALL ALONE!

GET MY CHARIOT READY! RALLY OUR ARMIES! ELEPHANTS, HORSES, CHARIOTS, ALL!

AT VIDARBHA, RUKMINI'S ANXIETY, INCREASED WITH EACH PASSING MOMENT.

THE HOUR IS DRAWING NEARER. WHY HAS MY LORD NOT YET COME?

DID MY MESSAGE DISGUST HIM? IF SO, THEN WHY HASN'T SUNANDA RETURNED?

AS SHE LOOKED OUT OF THE WINDOW FOR THE HUNDREDTH TIME, SHE SAW SUNANDA ENTER THE PALACE.

HE LOOKS CHEERFUL. HIS GAIT IS CONFIDENT. HE MUST BRING GOOD NEWS. HIS MISSION HAS BEEN SUCCESSFUL.

SHE TURNED TO HER MAIDS.

YOU MAY GO TO YOUR ROOMS. I WISH TO BE ALONE.

WHEN THEY LEFT, SHE RAN TO THE DOOR OF THE ROOM AND STOOD WAITING FOR THE BRAHMAN.

HE HAS COME, LITTLE ONE. EVERYTHING IS TO GO ACCORDING TO PLAN. HIS BROTHER TOO HAS COME WITH THE YADAVA FORCES.

NEWS OF KRISHNA'S ARRIVAL REACHED BHEESHMAKA, TOO.

KRISHNA HAS ARRIVED. HE HAS COME TO WITNESS THE WEDDING OF THE PRINCESS.

DARE I HOPE THAT HE HAS COME TO CARRY AWAY RUKMINI? DARE I?

HAVE A MANSION READY FOR HIM. FURNISH IT WITH EVERY LUXURY. I SHALL RIDE OUT TO RECEIVE HIM.

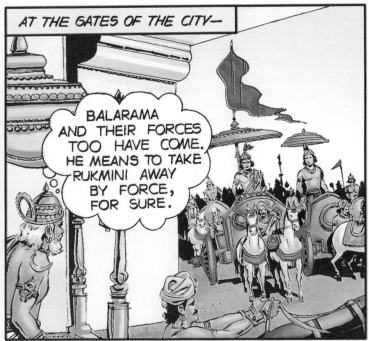

AT THE GATES OF THE CITY—

BALARAMA AND THEIR FORCES TOO HAVE COME. HE MEANS TO TAKE RUKMINI AWAY BY FORCE, FOR SURE.

WELCOME, O PRINCES! WE ARE HAPPY TO SEE YOU HERE. COME LET ME LEAD YOU TO THE PALACE WHERE YOU WILL STAY.

AS THEY RODE INTO THE CITY, THEY PASSED THE SHRINE OF GODDESS PARVATI, THE FAMILY DEITY OF THE ROYAL HOUSEHOLD.

AH! THAT IS THE TEMPLE RUKMINI WROTE ABOUT. HOW ANXIOUS MY DEAR ONE MUST BE.

*IN THOSE DAYS, A KSHATRIYA COULD CARRY AWAY HIS BRIDE, ESPECIALLY IF SHE SO DESIRED.

BALARAMA WAS CONCERNED ABOUT OTHER THINGS. HE TURNED TO BHEESHMAKA.

THE EMPEROR AND HIS MEN HAVE FLOODED THE CITY.

SHISHUPALA IS THE EMPEROR'S FAVOURITE. AND THE EMPEROR HAS MANY ALLIES.

THIS SHOULD HELP YOU PLAN YOUR STRATEGY.

MEANWHILE AT THE PALACE—

RUKMINI, YOUR CHARIOT HAS ARRIVED. ARE YOU READY?

I AM. LET US LEAVE.

ACCOMPANIED BY HER MAIDS, RUKMINI LEFT FOR THE SHRINE.

WHEN THEY REACHED THE GATES OF THE TEMPLE COURTYARD, SHE STEPPED OUT OF HER CHARIOT.

I DO NOT SEE KRISHNA AMONG THEM. THEY SAY HE IS DARK, WEARS A YELLOW ROBE, AND SPORTS A PEACOCK FEATHER IN HIS CROWN.

AS SHE WALKED TO THE TEMPLE, A MYRIAD EYES FOLLOWED HER EVERY MOVEMENT, DRINKING IN HER BEAUTY.

ALAS! SHE CAN NEVER BE MINE.

SHISHUPALA IS LUCKY. SHE IS THE VERY GODDESS OF WEALTH* INCARNATE.

* LAXMI

INSIDE THE TEMPLE—

I WORSHIP THEE, O FAITHFUL CONSORT OF SHIVA. I BOW TO THEE, THY LORD AND THY TWO SONS, GANESHA AND KARTIKEYA.

SHE WASHED THE GODDESS' FEET AND...

...PLACED OFFERINGS BEFORE HER.

THEN, OVERCOME BY THE THOUGHT THAT FILLED HER BEING, SHE PLEADED WITH THE GODDESS.

O GODDESS, PLEASE LET KRISHNA AND ONLY KRISHNA WIN AND WED ME.

HER WORSHIP OVER, SHE CAME OUT OF THE TEMPLE.

O GODDESS, DO NOT FAIL ME.

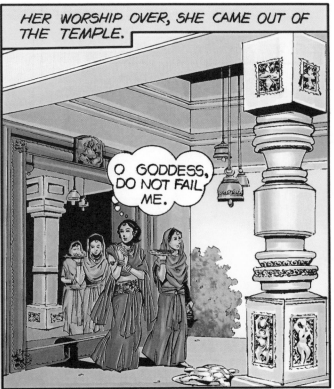

AS SHE WALKED TOWARDS THE GATE, HER EYES ANXIOUSLY SCANNED THE ASSEMBLY OF KINGS.

I DO NOT SEE HIM ANYWHERE.

HEAVY WAS HER HEART AND SLOW HER GAIT. THE CHARIOT LOOMED BEFORE HER ALL TOO SOON.

WILL KRISHNA EVER BECOME...

...MINE?

RUKMINI. IT'S ME. YOUR KRISHNA.

AND THE NEXT MOMENT SHE WAS SEATED NEXT TO HIM IN HIS CHARIOT.

STOP HIM!

RUKMINI! WAIT!

BUT KRISHNA'S CHARIOT SPED AWAY BLOWING DUST INTO THE EYES OF THE BEMUSED KINGS.

JARASANDHA WAS FURIOUS.

WHERE IS YOUR KSHATRIYA VALOUR? WHY DO YOU STAND THERE, AS IF YOU'VE LOST YOUR SENSES. PURSUE THEM!

JERKED INTO ACTION, THE KINGS CHARGED FORWARD.

BALARAMA TURNED TO KRISHNA.

THEY'RE GIVING CHASE. YOU RIDE ON. WE'LL FALL BACK AND DEAL WITH THEM.

WHEN RUKMINI LOOKED UP IN TERROR AT KRISHNA, HE LAUGHED HEARTILY AND ALLAYED HER FEARS.

DON'T BE ALARMED. OUR ARMIES WILL SOON ROUT THE ENEMY. BALA-RAMA WILL NOT LOSE HIS DEAR SISTER-IN-LAW SO EASILY.

HE WAS RIGHT.

CHASE THE JACKALS AWAY, MY MEN! SHOOT THEIR HORSES! DESTROY THEIR CHARIOTS!

WHILE BALARAMA WAS BUSY TACKLING JARASANDHA, SHISHUPALA AND THEIR HORDES, RUKMI CHARGED AHEAD AFTER KRISHNA'S VANISHING CHARIOT.

I WILL NOT RE-ENTER THE CAPITAL WITHOUT RUKMINI.

BALARAMA DID NOT TRY TO STOP HIM.

KRISHNA CAN DEAL WITH HIM, EVEN WITH RUKMINI IN HIS CHARIOT.

BALARAMA'S ONSLAUGHT WAS FIERCE.

LET US RETREAT, SHISHUPALA. THERE IS NO HOPE LEFT. THE COWHERDS ARE DETERMINED, RUKMINI IS LOST TO YOU.

ALAS! I FEEL AS IF MY WEDDED WIFE HAS BEEN ABDUCTED. SO SURE WAS I THAT SHE WAS MINE ALONE.

JARASANDHA TRIED TO CONSOLE HIM.

DON'T GRIEVE, SHISHUPALA. FORTUNE FAVOURED THEM AND THEY WON. WE SHALL CERTAINLY DEFEAT THEM WHEN OUR LUCK TURNS.

FULL OF HATRED FOR THE MAN WHO HAD WORSTED THEM, THE DISAPPOINTED SUITOR AND HIS WELL-WISHERS RETURNED TO THEIR CAPITALS.

MEANWHILE, RUKMI HAD ALMOST CAUGHT UP WITH KRISHNA.

TODAY I SHALL HUMBLE THE PRIDE OF THAT COWHERD WHO DARED ABDUCT MY SISTER.

SOON HIS CHARIOT WAS BUT A FEW FEET AWAY FROM KRISHNA.

FASTER... FASTER... FASTER...

STOP! STOP! WAIT, YOU DISGRACE TO THE RACE OF YADU! HOW DARE YOU KIDNAP MY SISTER, EVEN AS A CROW STEALS A SACRED OFFERING!

YOU WILY RASCAL. YOU HAVE PROVED YOUR CUNNING, NOW PROVE YOUR VALOUR.

RUKMI'S ARROW DID NOT EVEN MAKE A DENT IN KRISHNA'S ARMOUR.

KRISHNA PULLED OUT AN ARROW AND···

···LIFTED HIS BOW.

HE FIRST KILLED RUKMI'S HORSES AND···

···THEN SHATTERED HIS CHARIOT.

RUKMI TOOK COVER BEHIND THE DEBRIS...

...AND LIFTED HIS BOW...

...ONLY TO HAVE IT BROKEN TO BITS.

MAD WITH RAGE, RUKMI PICKED UP HIS SWORD...

...AND RUSHED TOWARDS KRISHNA.

THE NEXT MOMENT, HOWEVER FOUND HIM HOLDING BUT THE HILT.

AS HE THREW IT AWAY IN DISGUST, KRISHNA PICKED UP HIS SWORD AND...

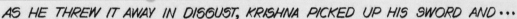

...WAS ABOUT TO RUSH TOWARDS HIM WHEN—

O VIRTUOUS LORD, PLEASE SPARE MY BROTHER. PLEASE DON'T KILL HIM.

ARISE, RUKMINI. FOR YOUR SAKE, RUKMI SHALL LIVE.

HE WENT UP TO RUKMI AND BOUND HIM WITH HIS OWN PRAPATA.*

I SHALL SHAVE OFF HALF HIS HAIR AND HALF HIS MOUSTACHE WITH THE BLADE OF MY SWORD. THERE COULD BE NO GREATER PUNISHMENT FOR A WARRIOR.

BALARAMA WAS HORRIFIED.

KRISHNA! WHAT ARE YOU DOING?

* CUMMERBUND.

KRISHNA, YOU HAVE PERFORMED AN IMPIOUS ACT; AN ACT DETESTED BY OUR RACE. TO DO WHAT YOU HAVE DONE TO A RELATIVE IS WORSE THAN KILLING HIM.

THEN HE TURNED TO RUKMINI.

PLEASE DO NOT TAKE OFFENCE, DEAR SISTER. YOUR BROTHER UNFORTUNATELY HAS REAPED THE FRUIT OF HIS OWN ACTIONS.

YOU ARE FREE TO GO, RUKMI.

ALAS! HE HAS ONLY ADDED INSULT TO INJURY. IT WERE BETTER THAT THEY HAD KILLED ME.

# KRISHNA AND JARASANDHA

LONG, LONG AGO, THE HANDSOME, WEALTHY AND POWERFUL KING BRIHADRATHA RULED OVER MAGADHA. HE WAS MARRIED TO THE BEAUTIFUL TWIN DAUGHTERS OF THE KING OF KASHI.

THOUGH HE HAD TWO QUEENS WHOM HE LOVED EQUALLY AND WHO LOVED HIM IN RETURN, THE KING HAD NO SONS. AS HE SAT BROODING ABOUT THIS ONE DAY—

LORD, THE ILLUSTRIOUS SAGE, CHANDAKAUSHIKA HAS COME TO THE CITY.

I MUST GO AND PAY MY RESPECTS TO HIM.

TAKING MANY GIFTS WITH HIM, BRIHADRATHA WENT TO SEE THE SAGE. LATER—

O KING OF KINGS, YOU HAVE PLEASED ME WELL. ASK A BOON OF ME.

O RISHI, WHAT USE HAVE I FOR A BOON? I AM ABOUT TO RENOUNCE THE KINGDOM AND GO INTO THE FORESTS. CURSED AS I AM, I HAVE NO SON.

THE RISHI CLOSED HIS EYES. SUDDENLY —

LET YOUR WIFE EAT THIS AND OBTAIN A SON.

AS BRIHADRATHA WALKED AWAY WITH THE MANGO —

I CANNOT GIVE THE FRUIT TO ONE AND MAKE THE OTHER UNHAPPY. THEY SHALL EACH HAVE HALF OF IT.

AND THE KING DIVIDED THE MANGO BETWEEN HIS WIVES.

BUT WHEN THE QUEENS DELIVERED, THEY HAD ONLY HALF A BABY EACH.

ALAS! I SHOULD HAVE LET YOU EAT THE WHOLE FRUIT.

NO, SISTER. I SHOULD HAVE LET YOU EAT IT.

IT'S TOO LATE NOW. WHAT SHALL WE DO WITH THESE?

LET'S CAST THEM OFF. WHAT ELSE CAN WE DO?

SO THE MIDWIVES CARRIED THE TWO HALVES AND THREW THEM INTO THE BACKYARD OF THE QUEENS' APARTMENTS.

A FEW HOURS LATER, THE RAKSHASI, JARA, WHO LIVED ON FLESH AND BLOOD, CAME BY.

MM-M-M! HUMAN FLESH! I SMELL HUMAN FLESH!

HER NOSE LED HER TO THE TWO BUNDLES OF FLESH.

WHAT! ONE BODY RENT IN TWO. I'LL JOIN THE HALVES. IT WILL BE EASIER TO CARRY ONE BUNDLE.

THE MOMENT SHE JOINED THE TWO PIECES, THE BABY CAME TO LIFE AND ROARED.

AA-A-AH! GR-R-R-R!

HEARING THE ROAR, THE KING, HIS QUEENS, THE MIDWIVES, THE SERVANTS, ALL CAME RUNNING OUT.

ISN'T THAT THE VIRTUOUS KING WHO LONGED FOR A SON. I WILL GIVE HIM BACK HIS CHILD.

WHEN THEY REACHED HER—

O KING, I, JARA, HAVE SAVED YOUR SON FOR YOU. TAKE HIM.

GOOD LADY, SINCE IT WAS YOU WHO PUT HIM TOGETHER AND MADE HIM COMPLETE, HE SHALL BE NAMED JARASANDHA.

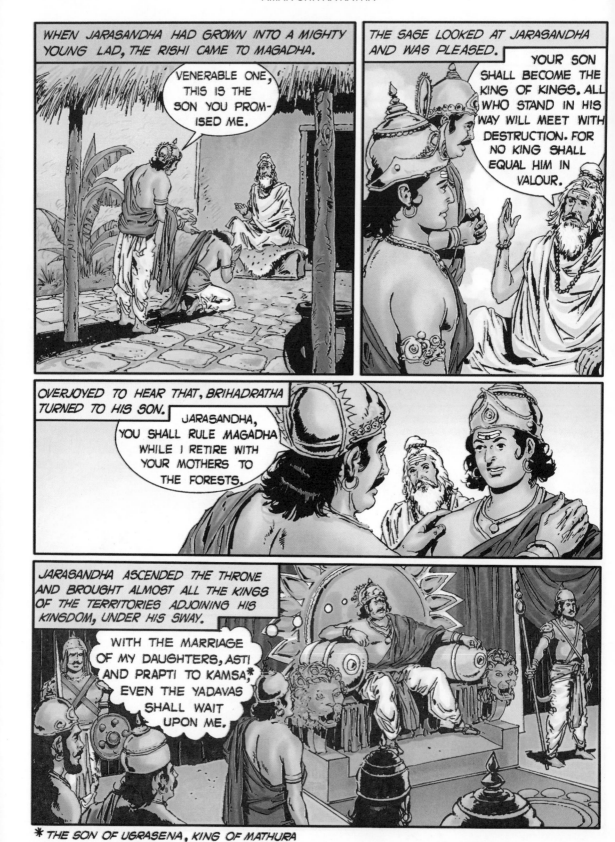

WHEN JARASANDHA HAD GROWN INTO A MIGHTY YOUNG LAD, THE RISHI CAME TO MAGADHA.

VENERABLE ONE, THIS IS THE SON YOU PROMISED ME.

THE SAGE LOOKED AT JARASANDHA AND WAS PLEASED.

YOUR SON SHALL BECOME THE KING OF KINGS. ALL WHO STAND IN HIS WAY WILL MEET WITH DESTRUCTION. FOR NO KING SHALL EQUAL HIM IN VALOUR.

OVERJOYED TO HEAR THAT, BRIHADRATHA TURNED TO HIS SON.

JARASANDHA, YOU SHALL RULE MAGADHA WHILE I RETIRE WITH YOUR MOTHERS TO THE FORESTS.

JARASANDHA ASCENDED THE THRONE AND BROUGHT ALMOST ALL THE KINGS OF THE TERRITORIES ADJOINING HIS KINGDOM, UNDER HIS SWAY.

WITH THE MARRIAGE OF MY DAUGHTERS, ASTI AND PRAPTI TO KAMSA,* EVEN THE YADAVAS SHALL WAIT UPON ME.

* THE SON OF UGRASENA, KING OF MATHURA

70

BUT KAMSA WAS AN EVIL KING. HE DEPOSED HIS FATHER AND PERSECUTED HIS OWN SUBJECTS.

WITH THE MIGHTY JARASANDHA AS MY FATHER-IN-LAW, I NEED FEAR NONE. NONE, EXCEPT MY NEPHEW, KRISHNA.

BEFORE KRISHNA WAS BORN, IT HAD BEEN PROPHESIED THAT HE WOULD KILL THE EVIL KAMSA.

FATE AND THE GODS CONSPIRED AGAINST ME AND FOILED MY ATTEMPTS TO DESTROY THE CHILD.

THEY SAY, HE IS LIVING AMONG THE GOPAS* OF BRINDAVAN WITH HIS BROTHER BALARAMA. I SHALL INVITE HIM TO MATHURA AND KILL HIM.

BUT AT THE FATED HOUR, IT WAS KAMSA WHO MET WITH HIS END AT KRISHNA'S HANDS.

UGRASENA WAS RESTORED TO THE THRONE. WHILE ALL MATHURA REJOICED...

* COWHERDS

...AT MAGADHA, JARASANDHA WAS INFURIATED WHEN HE SAW HIS WIDOWED DAUGHTERS.

DO NOT WEEP, MY CHILDREN. I SHALL AVENGE THE DEATH OF YOUR HUSBAND.

HE TURNED TO HIS COMMANDER.

INFORM OUR ALLIES! RALLY OUR ARMIES! I SHALL RID THE EARTH OF THAT VILE YADAVA, KRISHNA, AND ALL HIS TRIBE!

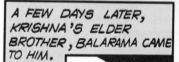
A FEW DAYS LATER, KRISHNA'S ELDER BROTHER, BALARAMA CAME TO HIM.

JARASANDHA AND HIS ALLIES HAVE BESIEGED THE CITY.

IT WAS TO BE EXPECTED. LET US GO OUT AND GAUGE THE STRENGTH OF THEIR ARMIES.

AS THEY STOOD SURVEYING THE SCENE, TWO CHARIOTS SUDDENLY DESCENDED FROM THE HEAVENS, FULL OF DIVINE WEAPONS.

LOOK, BALARAMA! CHARIOTS! ARMOUR! WEAPONS!

QUICK! LET US TAKE WITH US THE MEN WE HAVE AND SAVE OUR RACE.

AS THEY RODE OUT, FOLLOWED BY THEIR SMALL ARMY—

I WILL DESTROY THEM ALL EXCEPT JARASANDHA. WHEN HE COMES BACK WITH MORE ALLIES, WE SHALL DESTROY THEM TOO.

THE TWO BROTHERS CONFRONTED JARASANDHA. KRISHNA BLEW HIS CONCH, INVITING THE KING TO BEGIN THE ATTACK.

DO YOU REALLY WANT TO FIGHT ? MY ARROWS WILL SEND YOU TO HEAVEN...

THE VALIANT DO NOT BRAG BUT PROVE THEIR MIGHT IN ACTION.

WITHOUT ANOTHER WORD, JARASANDHA AND HIS HUGE ARMY CHARGED.

BUT KRISHNA DREW OUT HIS BOW AND LET FLY HIS ARROWS IN SUCH QUICK SUCCESSION...

...THAT THE FIELD WAS SOON STREWN WITH THE BODIES OF MEN, HORSES, ELEPHANTS AND CHARIOTS.

THE ALLIES AND THEIR ARMIES BEGAN TO FLEE.

MEANWHILE, SWINGING HIS MACE, BALARAMA WHO HAD TAKEN ON JARASANDHA'S OWN ARMY, SOON DESTROYED IT AND...

... SEIZED JARASANDHA.

HE WAS ABOUT TO BIND HIM WITH ROPES, WHEN —

NO, BALARAMA. LET HIM GO. LET US INFORM UGRASENA OF OUR VICTORY AND PRESENT HIM WITH OUR BOOTY.

UTTERLY HUMILIATED, JARASANDHA RETURNED TO GIRIVRAJA, HIS CAPITAL.

I WILL NOT GIVE UP. I WILL GO BACK WITH NEW ARMIES AND TEACH THE YADAVAS A LESSON.

JARASANDHA MADE SEVENTEEN ATTEMPTS TO AVENGE THE DEATH OF HIS SON-IN-LAW AND HIS OWN SUCCESSIVE HUMILIATIONS; AND SEVENTEEN TIMES DID KRISHNA DECIMATE HIS ARMIES, SPARING HIM ALONE.

MEANWHILE, KALAYAVANA, THE INVINCIBLE, WAS BRAGGING ABOUT HIS VALOUR TO SAGE NARADA.

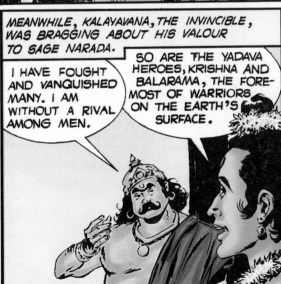

I HAVE FOUGHT AND VANQUISHED MANY. I AM WITHOUT A RIVAL AMONG MEN.

SO ARE THE YADAVA HEROES, KRISHNA AND BALARAMA, THE FOREMOST OF WARRIORS ON THE EARTH'S SURFACE.

THE REMARK WAS ENOUGH TO BRING KALAYAVANA WITH HIS BARBARIAN HORDES TO MATHURA.

AS HE STOOD OUTSIDE THE GATES OF THE CITY, CHALLENGING THE YADAVAS...

... A MESSENGER RAN UP TO KRISHNA AND BALARAMA.

JARASANDHA IS MARCHING TOWARDS THE CITY, HE SHOULD BE HERE IN A DAY OR TWO.

THIS IS UNFORTUNATE! WHILE WE ARE BUSY FIGHTING THE YAVANA, JARASANDHA WILL KILL OR IMPRISON OUR PEOPLE!

WHAT SHALL WE DO?

WE WILL HAVE TO TRANSPORT THEM TO A SAFE PLACE BEFORE JARASANDHA ARRIVES.

KRISHNA HAD BUT TO THINK ABOUT IT AND THE FORTRESS OF DWARAKA ROSE IN THE WESTERN SEA.

USING HIS YOGIC POWER, KRISHNA TRANSPORTED THE PEOPLE, THE CATTLE AND THE WEALTH OF MATHURA TO DWARAKA.

THEN, ALONG WITH BALARAMA AND A SMALL ARMY OF YADAVAS WHO CHOSE TO STAY AND FIGHT, HE CAME OUT OF THE CITY GATES, UNARMED AND ON FOOT.

WHILE BALARAMA AND THE ARMY MADE STRAIGHT FOR THE YAVANA HORDES...

...ASSUMING HIS DIVINE*FORM, KRISHNA WALKED TOWARDS KALAYAVANA.

THIS IS THE YADAVA, JUST AS NARADA DESCRIBED HIM. I TOO SHALL DISMOUNT AND ATTACK HIM, UNARMED.

* KRISHNA BEING AN INCARNATION OF LORD VISHNU

LAYING DOWN HIS WEAPONS, KALAYAVANA DISMOUNTED...

...AND RUSHED FORWARD. BUT JUST AS HE WAS ABOUT TO SEIZE HIM...

...KRISHNA SUDDENLY TURNED ROUND...

...AND BEGAN WALKING.

DO NOT RUN AWAY, O YADAVA. IT DOES NOT BECOME A HERO LIKE YOU.

I'LL SOON OVERTAKE YOU, O COWARDLY YADAVA, AND REMAIN UNRIVALLED AMONG MEN.

AND HE BEGAN WALKING FASTER. FINDING KRISHNA ALMOST WITHIN HIS GRASP, HE LURCHED FORWARD...

...ONLY TO GRAB THE EMPTY AIR.

AFTER WALKING FOR MILES, THEY CAME TO THE MOUNTAIN CAVE OF SAGE MUCHUKUNDA.

AH! NOW YOU WILL NOT ESCAPE ME!

GROPING IN THE DARK, THE YAVANA FOLLOWED KRISHNA.

SHOW YOURSELF, O BRAVE YADAVA!

GRADUALLY THE YAVANA GOT USED TO THE THE DARK. HE SAW A MAN SLEEPING IN A CORNER OF THE CAVE.

AH! THERE! SO THE COWARD IS ALSO A WEAKLING. HE LEADS ME THIS FAR AND THEN FALLS, EXHAUSTED.

MISTAKING THE SLEEPING FIGURE FOR KRISHNA, HE KICKED IT.

COME ON! WAKE UP AND FIGHT!

THE SLEEPING FIGURE SAT UP AND SLOWLY OPENED HIS EYES.

WHO DARES DISTURB THE SLUMBER OF MUCHUKUNDA?

AS HE LOOKED AROUND FOR THE CULPRIT, HIS BURNING GAZE FELL ON KALAYAVANA.

MUCHUKUNDA GAZED LONG AND HARD...

...AND ALL THAT WAS LEFT OF THE YAVANA WAS A HANDFUL OF ASHES.

BALARAMA, MEANWHILE WAS STRUGGLING WITH THE YAVANA'S HORDES. HE HAD ALMOST GIVEN UP HOPE, WHEN —

AH! KRISHNA! KRISHNA HAS RETURNED!

ALAS! THE YADAVA RETURNS ALONE. OUR LORD IS DEAD.

TOGETHER THE TWO BROTHERS SOON KILLED THE ENTIRE ARMY.

AS THEY WERE RETURNING TO DWARAKA WITH THE TREASURES OF THE YAVANAS —

LOOK! JARASANDHA! WITH MORE MEN THAN···

I'VE HAD ENOUGH OF FIGHTING, KRISHNA. LET'S FLEE TO DWARAKA.

THEY BEGAN TO RUN.

HA! HA! LOOK AT THE BRAVE YADAVA HEROES! LOOK AT THEM FLEE! THIS TIME I WILL NOT RETURN WITHOUT KILLING THEM.

AND JARASANDHA AND HIS ARMY GAVE CHASE.

FOR MILES KRISHNA AND BALARAMA RAN, WITH JARA-SANDHA AND HIS HUGE ARMY FOLLOWING CLOSE BEHIND. AT LAST—

AH! MOUNT PRAVARSHANA! LET'S CLIMB IT. THEY WILL FIND IT DIFFICULT TO FOLLOW US UP.

FOR A MOMENT JARASANDHA WAS DUMB WITH FURY TO SEE HIS QUARRY ESCAPE. THEN HE GAVE ORDERS.

SET FIRE TO THE MOUNTAIN! BURN THE VILE YADAVAS ALIVE!

AS THE FLAMES ENVELOPED THE MOUNTAIN, CLOUDING THE ENEMIES' VISION—

QUICK! NOW IS THE CHANCE FOR US TO MAKE GOOD OUR ESCAPE!

THE TWO BROTHERS TOOK ONE MIGHTY LEAP FROM THE MOUNTAIN TOP...

...CROSSED THE ARMIES SURROUNDING THE BASE OF THE MOUNTAIN...

...LANDED ON THE PLAIN, UNNOTICED BY JARASANDHA'S MEN...

...AND MADE THEIR WAY TO DWARAKA.

MEANWHILE, AS THE FIRE ON THE MOUNTAIN BLAZED HIGH—

KAMSA'S DEATH HAS BEEN AVENGED! HIS MURDERER HAS BEEN BURNT ALIVE! LET US RETURN TO MATHURA!

LATER, WHEN JARASANDHA LEARNT THAT THEY WERE NOT DEAD—

ALL THE SAME, I HAVE WON A BATTLE AGAINST THE HATED YADAVA! I HAVE CHASED HIS TRIBE OUT OF MATHURA!

THIS ONE VICTORY MADE JARASANDHA CONCEITED AND AMBITIOUS.

I AM NOW THE MOST POWERFUL KING ON EARTH. I SHALL CAPTURE ALL THE KINGS WHO OWE ALLEGIANCE TO THE YADAVAS AND SACRIFICE THEM.

JARASANDHA DID NOT WASTE ANY TIME. SOON—

AH! ONE MORE. THE NUMBERS SWELL DAILY. MY SACRIFICE SHALL BE UNEQUALLED BY ANY THAT HAS BEEN OR EVER WILL BE PERFORMED.

MEANWHILE, KRISHNA'S COUSINS, THE PANDAVAS, HAD JUST ACQUIRED THE KINGDOM OF INDRAPRASTHA. EVERYONE WAS ANXIOUS FOR YUDHISHTHIRA TO PERFORM THE RAJASUYA SACRIFICE.

DO NOT DELAY, O KING. PERFORM THE SACRIFICE AND BECOME LORD OF THE EARTH.

TO PERFORM THE RAJASUYA IS THE PRIVILEGE OF AN EMPEROR. AND SO JARASANDHA WILL HAVE TO BE DEFEATED. LET ME CONSULT KRISHNA ON THIS.

WHEN KRISHNA CAME AND YUDHISHTHIRA ASKED HIM HIS OPINION —

TO PERFORM THE RAJASUYA YOU WILL HAVE TO KILL JARASANDHA AND RELEASE THE KINGS IMPRISONED BY HIM.

SINCE EVEN YOU WERE ALARMED BY HIS MIGHT, HOW CAN I EVER HOPE TO KILL HIM?

AT THAT MOMENT, BHEEMA*WHO HAD BEEN LISTENING QUIETLY, SUDDENLY SPOKE UP.

BETWEEN KRISHNA, ARJUNA AND ME, WE CAN EASILY KILL THE EVIL JARASANDHA. PLEASE PERMIT US TO TRY.

YES. LET US GO. HE WHO KILLS JARASANDHA AND FREES HIS VICTIMS, WILL EARN IMMORTAL FAME.

BUT EVEN THEN YUDHISHTHIRA HESITATED.

NO. I CANNOT SEND YOU TO CERTAIN DEATH FOR THE SAKE OF IMPERIAL GLORY.

ARJUNA, THE THIRD PANDAVA, THEN HAD HIS SAY.

IF WE DO NOT UNDERTAKE THE TASK WHEN WE HAVE THE ABILITY TO DO SO, WE WILL EARN THE CONTEMPT OF ALL. PERMIT US TO GO.

YES. IF YOU HAVE ANY FAITH IN ME...

KRISHNA, MY FAITH IN YOU IS FIRM! TAKE MY BROTHERS AND GO. MAY SUCCESS BE YOURS.

* THE SECOND OF THE FIVE PANDAVAS.

HAVING RECEIVED YUDHISHTHIRA'S CONSENT AND BLESSINGS, KRISHNA, ARJUNA, AND BHEEMA SET OUT FOR MAGADHA, DISGUISED AS BRAHMANS.

THEY REACHED JARA-SANDHA'S PALACE AT THE HOUR WHEN HE ENTERTAINED PETITIONS.

O KING, WE HAVE COME FROM AFAR FOR A DEFI-NITE PURPOSE. SO PLEASE SAY YOU WILL GRANT US OUR REQUEST.

JARASANDHA, HOWEVER, WAS NOT WHOLLY TAKEN IN.

THEIR BEARING... THOSE SCARRED FORE-ARMS... THEY ARE NO BRAHMANS. I THINK I'VE SEEN THEM BEFORE.

THEY HAVE COME DISGUISED, OUT OF FEAR OF ME. SINCE THEY HAVE TAKEN THE TROUBLE TO COME HERE, I WILL GRANT THEM WHATEVER THEY ASK OF ME.

O BRAHMANS, SEEK WHATEVER YOU DESIRE. I AM PREPARED TO GIVE YOU EVERYTHING, EVEN MY HEAD.

THEN GRANT ONE OF US A SINGLE COMBAT WITH YOU.

BUT HOW CAN I, THE KING OF KINGS, LIFT A WEAPON AGAINST A BRAHMAN?

WE ARE NO BRAHMANS. THIS IS BHEEMA, SON OF KUNTI···

···THIS, ARJUNA, HIS YOUNGER BROTHER. AND I AM KRISHNA, THEIR COUSIN AND YOUR SWORN ENEMY.

JARASANDHA LAUGHED CONTEMPTUOUSLY.

FOOLS! IF YOU SEEK COMBAT, I WILL CERTAINLY FIGHT. BUT · · ·

· · · NOT WITH YOU, KRISHNA. YOU ARE A COWARD.

AS FOR ARJUNA, HE IS TOO YOUNG. HE IS NO MATCH FOR ME. BHEEMA ALONE IS MY EQUAL. I'LL TAKE HIM ON.

JARASANDHA THREW A HUGE MACE TO BHEEMA · · ·

... AND TOOK ANOTHER FOR HIMSELF.

COME, LET US GO OUT OF THE CITY INTO THE ARENA.

ONCE INSIDE THE ARENA, THE TWO WARRIORS BEGAN THEIR FIGHT.

THEY HURLED THEIR MACES AT EACH OTHER...

... TILL THE MACES BROKE.

FULL OF RAGE, THEY RUSHED AT EACH OTHER, HITTING OUT WITH THEIR FISTS OF STEEL. THE BLOWS PRODUCED SOUNDS AS SHARP AS THUNDER-CLAPS.

FOR TWENTY-SEVEN DAYS THEY FOUGHT.

BUT SO WELL-MATCHED WERE THEY, THAT NEITHER SUCCUMBED TO THE OTHER'S BLOWS.

AT LAST, ON THE TWENTY-EIGHTH DAY, AS BHEEMA WAS ABOUT TO ENTER THE ARENA—

KRISHNA, I REMAIN UNDEFEATED, BUT I CANNOT OVERTHROW JARASANDHA IN A DUEL.

KRISHNA, WHO KNEW THE SECRET OF JARA-SANDHA'S BIRTH, DECIDED THAT IT WAS TIME TO END THE BATTLE.

FOR HAVING ENGAGED JARASANDHA IN COMBAT FOR TWENTY-SEVEN DAYS, BHEEMA WILL ACHIEVE ENOUGH FAME. IT'S TIME I SHOWED HIM HOW TO KILL THE EVIL KING.

WITHOUT SAYING A WORD, KRISHNA PICKED UP A TWIG AND...

...SPLIT IT IN TWO, LENGTHWAYS.

AH! NOW I HAVE IT.

BHEEMA STRODE INTO THE ARENA WITH FRESH CONFIDENCE.

THE FIRST OPPORTUNITY I GET, I MUST SEIZE HIM BY HIS FEET AND THROW HIM TO THE GROUND. THE REST WILL BE EASY!

JARASANDHA RUSHED TOWARDS HIM.

BUT BHEEMA DEFTLY STEPPED ASIDE.

AS JARASANDHA STAGGERED WITH THE MOMENTUM OF HIS CHARGE...

...BHEEMA SEIZED HIM BY THE LEG...

...AND HURLED HIM TO THE GROUND.

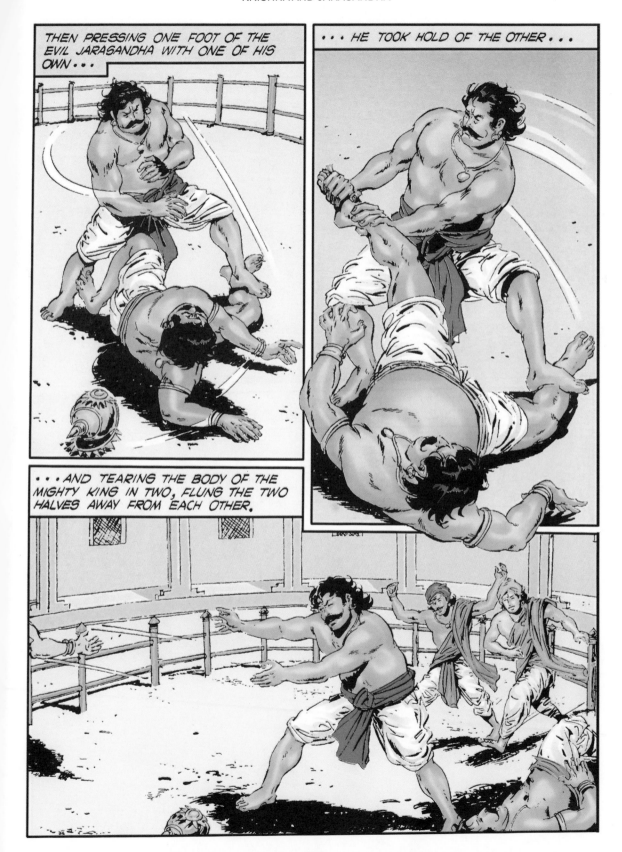

GREAT WAS THE OUTCRY AMONG THE CITIZENS OF GIRIVRAJA WHEN THEY LEARNT THAT JARASANDHA, THEIR INVINCIBLE KING, HAD FALLEN. KRISHNA WENT TO JARASANDHA'S SON.

YOU WILL HAVE TO LIBERATE OUR ALLIES AND ACCEPT YUDHISHTHIRA AS YOUR EMPEROR. IF YOU DO, WE WILL INSTALL YOU ON YOUR FATHER'S THRONE.

I WILL DO AS YOU SAY.

AFTER INSTALLING HIM ON THE THRONE, KRISHNA AND THE TWO PANDAVAS RETURNED TO INDRAPRASTHA.

YUDHISHTHIRA, JARASANDHA HAS BEEN KILLED AND THE IMPRISONED KINGS LIBERATED. HIS SON ACCEPTS YOUR SUPREMACY. YOU ARE NOW THE KING OF KINGS. YOU MAY PERFORM THE RAJASUYA SACRIFICE.

# A Debt to Krishna

Once, the king of Ambalapuzzha was callenged to a game of chess by an old sage. The prize, if he won, would be one grain of rice on the first square of the chessboard, two on the second, four on the third and so on, doubling the amount on the previous square. The king brashly agreed.

The sage won the game. The king started placing the rice grains and was shocked to see their number grow exponentially. By the end, he owed trillions of tons of rice!

Amused at the king's confusion, the sage revealed himself to be Krishna! "You don't have to give it all today," he said. "Just provide payasam to every pilgrim who comes to my temple here, in search of comfort."

Krishna's wish is honoured even today and payasam is served freely to all who visit the Ambalapuzzha Krishna temple.

# KRISHNA AND NARAKASURA

IN HIS VARAHA AVATAR,*VISHNU LIFTED BHOOMI DEVI FROM THE DEPTHS OF THE OCEAN. SOON AFTER THAT A SON WAS BORN TO BHOOMI DEVI. HE CAME TO BE KNOWN AS NARAKASURA. THOUGH HE WAS THE SON OF A DIVINITY AND A VIRTUOUS MOTHER, NARAKA UNFORTUNATELY TURNED OUT TO BE A VICIOUS ASURA...

...WHO TOOK PLEASURE IN TERRORISING THE INHABITANTS OF ALL THE THREE WORLDS.

*THIRD INCARNATION OF VISHNU
IN THE FORM OF A BOAR

KINGS AND SAGES, RAKSHASAS AND DEVAS ALIKE, FEARED HIM.

IT'S NARAKASURA! HE'S BACK!

DON'T LET THE WOMEN COME OUT. GUARD THEIR APARTMENTS.

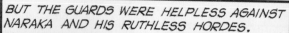

BUT THE GUARDS WERE HELPLESS AGAINST NARAKA AND HIS RUTHLESS HORDES.

ROUND UP THE CHARIOTS AND HORSES! SEIZE THE MAIDENS. THEY SHALL ADORN MY PALACE.

LATER, AT NARAKA'S CAPITAL, PRAGJYOTISHA—

HOW MANY MAIDENS HAVE WE CAPTURED SO FAR?

SIXTEEN THOUSAND AND ONE HUNDRED, O KING.

ENOUGH! HOW MANY FOUR-TUSKED ELEPHANTS DOES INDRA HAVE?

THOUSANDS, MY LORD—ALL DESCENDANTS OF INDRA'S MOUNT, AIRAVATA.

THEN ON TO AMARAVATI*! THOSE ELEPHANTS SHALL ADORN MY STABLES.

AS NARAKASURA RODE INTO AMARAVATI...

...AND UP TO INDRA'S STABLES...

* INDRA'S CAPITAL

. . . INDRA COULD ONLY FUME WITH IMPOTENT FURY.

HE'S TAKING AWAY MY ELEPHANTS! BUT WHAT CAN I DO? I DARE NOT OPPOSE THE ASURA. HE IS INVINCIBLE.

THUS DID THE WICKED NARAKA HARASS THE DEVAS.

THEN FOR SOME REASON THE ASURA LAY LOW FOR A WHILE.

NARAKA SEEMS TO HAVE TIRED OF HIS WICKED WAYS, AT LAST.

YES. WE HAVE NOT KNOWN SUCH PEACE FOR A LONG WHILE.

WE SHALL HOLD A FEAST TO CELEBRATE OUR NEW-FOUND PEACE.

A FEW DAYS LATER, AMARAVATI, WORE A FESTIVE LOOK. THE SWEET SCENT OF THE PARIJATA BLOOMS FILLED THE AIR. ALL THE DEVAS, WEARING THEIR BEST ORNAMENTS, ASSEMBLED TO WATCH THE APSARAS PERFORM.

*LORD OF THE HYDROSPHERE

AS NARAKA CHARGED TOWARDS VARUNA, A DAZZLING FLASH BLINDED HIM FOR A MOMENT.

THE MOTHER OF THE DEVAS HAS WORN HER PRECIOUS EAR-RINGS!

THOSE EAR-RINGS LACK LUSTRE ON YOU, O MOTHER OF THE COWARDLY DEVAS.

HE RUSHED FORWARD AND SNATCHED THE EAR-RINGS.

I SHALL KEEP THEM.

AND MOUNTING HIS CHARIOT...

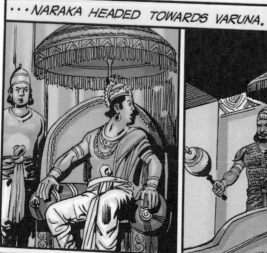

...NARAKA HEADED TOWARDS VARUNA.

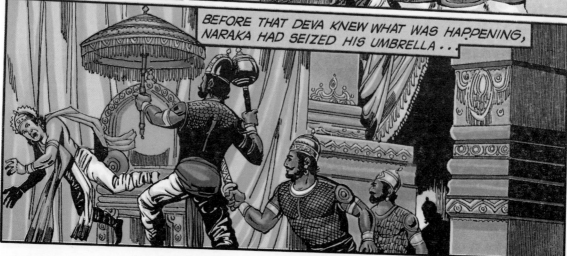

BEFORE THAT DEVA KNEW WHAT WAS HAPPENING, NARAKA HAD SEIZED HIS UMBRELLA...

...AND WAS RIDING TOWARDS INDRA.

HE'S COMING FOR ME! I'D BETTER FLEE.

INDRA MOUNTED AIRAVATA...

...AND ROSE INTO THE AIR.

THE ARROGANT ASURA HAS DARED LAY HIS IMPURE HANDS ON MY MOTHER'S EAR-RINGS! HE HAS GONE TOO FAR.

HE MUST BE TAUGHT A LESSON. AND THERE IS ONLY ONE WHO CAN DO IT. I WILL SEEK HIS HELP.

WHEN AN AGITATED INDRA BURST INTO THE PALACE AT DWARAKA, KRISHNA WAS SEATED WITH SATYABHAMA.

WHAT'S THE MATTER? WHY DO YOU LOOK SO PALE?

IT'S THE ASURA, NARAKA.

BHOOMI DEVI'S SON? WHAT HAS HE DONE?

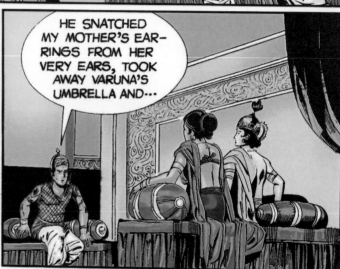

HE SNATCHED MY MOTHER'S EAR-RINGS FROM HER VERY EARS, TOOK AWAY VARUNA'S UMBRELLA AND....

...AND DROVE ME OUT OF AMARAVATI. YOU MUST KILL THAT SINFUL WRETCH. ONLY YOU CAN DO IT.

WHERE IS HE NOW?

HE HAS GONE BACK TO HIS IMPREGNABLE CAPITAL, PRA-GJYOTISHA.

NARAKASURA HAS INVITED HIS OWN DEATH BY DARING TO LAY HIS HANDS ON MOTHER ADITI'S EAR-RINGS.

*AS SOON AS KRISHNA PICKED UP HIS CONCH AND HIS WEAPONS, GARUDA APPEARED BEFORE HIM.*

MOUNTED ON GARUDA, I'LL FINISH OFF THE EVIL ONE.

YOU WILL HAVE TO SURMOUNT THE BARRIERS OF MOUNTAINS, WEAPONS, WATER, FIRE AND WIND THAT ENCIRCLE HIS CAPITAL. AND THE FIVE-HEADED ASURA, MURA, GUARDS THE GATES OF HIS PALACE.

AS KRISHNA WAS ABOUT TO TELL INDRA THAT HE WAS AWARE OF ALL THAT, HE SAW SATYABHAMA POUTING.

SATYABHAMA RESENTS THIS RUDE INTERRUPTION. THE GENTLE ONE CANNOT BEAR THIS SUDDEN SEPARATION. I'LL TAKE HER WITH ME.

WITHOUT UTTERING A WORD, HE CAUGHT THE PLEASANTLY SURPRISED SATYABHAMA BY THE WAIST...

...AND SWUNG HER ONTO GARUDA.

HE THEN SEATED HIMSELF BEHIND HER.

GARUDA SOARED INTO THE AIR.

AS THEY NEARED PRAGJYOTISHA, GARUDA'S BEAK SUDDENLY HIT SOMETHING HARD.

WHICHEVER WAY HE TURNED, HUGE MOUNTAINS ROSE BEFORE HIM, BLOCKING HIS PATH.

LORD, I CANNOT MOVE FORWARD.

KRISHNA WAS UNPERTURBED. HE SWUNG OUT HIS MACE...

111

... AND WITHIN MINUTES THE MOUNTAINS WERE SHATTERED.

FLY ON, GARUDA! WE'VE BROKEN THE FIRST BARRIER.

FILLED WITH RENEWED ENERGY, GARUDA FLEW ON.

SUDDENLY —

LORD! SAVE ME!

THIS FIRST ARROW WAS FOLLOWED BY A BARRAGE OF WEAPONS OF EVERY DESCRIPTION.

WAIT, GARUDA. DON'T TRY TO BREAK THROUGH.

KRISHNA SHOT THE ARROWS FROM HIS INEXHAUSTIBLE QUIVER, IN SUCH QUICK SUCCESSION...

...THAT EVERY SINGLE WEAPON WAS DESTROYED BEFORE IT COULD REACH ANYWHERE NEAR GARUDA OR SATYABHAMA.

THAT'S THE LAST OF THEM! YOU MAY PROCEED, GARUDA.

GARUDA, FLAPPED HIS WINGS HARD...

...AND FLEW ON...

...ONLY TO BE PUSHED BACK BY A SUDDEN SURGE OF HUGE WAVES OF WATER.

GARUDA! LORD! IT'S THE DELUGE!

UNPERTURBED, KRISHNA RAISED HIS FINGER.

THE NEXT MOMENT HIS FLYING DISCUS CUT THROUGH THE WAVES...

...BREAKING THEM INTO GENTLE, LIFE-GIVING RAIN.

REFRESHED BY THE COOL SHOWERS, GARUDA WAS ABOUT TO FLY ON WHEN···

···A HUGE BLAZE EVAPORATED THE RAIN AND···

···SENT OUT LEAPING TONGUES OF FLAME TO SCORCH THE INTRUDERS.

BUT THE WHIRLING DISCUS WITH ITS INCREASING MOMENTUM CUT THROUGH THE FLAMES.

GARUDA DARTED FORWARD...

...ONLY TO BE CONFRONTED BY THE WILDEST OF GALES...

...WHICH KEPT SWEEPING HIM BACK INTO THE FIRE.

BUT THE DISCUS, WHOSE MOMENTUM NOW MATCHED THAT OF THE CYCLONIC WINDS, WHIRRED THROUGH THE CURRENTS IN THE OPPOSITE DIRECTION.

THUS THE STORMY WINDS WERE TAMED AND GARUDA FLEW ON.

SOON—

AH! THE OUTER GATES OF NARAKA'S PALACE! THERE LIES MURA, DEEP IN SLEEP. I SHALL ROUSE HIM OUT OF HIS COMPLACENCY.

KRISHNA RAISED HIS CONCH AND SENT OUT A TRIUMPHANT BLARE.

117

AS THE SOUND RENT THE AIR, MURA, NARAKA'S FIVE-HEADED ASURA GUARD, AWOKE WITH A START...

...TO SEE GARUDA HOVERING ABOVE HIM.

IT'S KRISHNA! HE'S COME TO SLAY NARAKA. BUT HE'LL HAVE TO KILL ME FIRST.

RAISING HIS GLITTERING TRIDENT...

...MURA CHARGED TOWARDS KRISHNA.

BUT WITH TWO ARROWS SHOT IN QUICK SUCCESSION...

...KRISHNA SPLIT THE WEAPON INTO THREE BEFORE IT COULD TOUCH THEM.

THEN HE SENT HIS STINGING ARROWS INTO THE FIVE GAPING MOUTHS OF THE ASURA.

ROARING WITH PAIN, MURA FLUNG HIS MACE AT KRISHNA...

...ONLY TO HAVE IT BLASTED AGAINST KRISHNA'S RAISED ONE.

INSIDE THE PALACE, THE CLASH OF THE MACES AWOKE NARAKA.

WHAT WAS THAT?

HE WALKED UP TO THE WINDOW AND LOOKED OUT. HE WAS ALARMED BY THE SIGHT THAT MET HIS EYES.

IT'S KRISHNA! WILL MURA BE ABLE TO VANQUISH HIM?

AS NARAKA WATCHED, MURA RUSHED FORWARD BLINDLY TO CRUSH KRISHNA.

THAT WILL BE THE END OF KRISHNA!

BUT SMILING ALL THE WHILE, WITH ONE ARM PROTECTIVELY AROUND SATYABHAMA, KRISHNA RAISED HIS FINGER.

HIS DISCUS CAME SAILING THROUGH THE AIR...

...AND THE NEXT MOMENT, THE WICKED MURA'S HEADS WERE SEVERED FROM HIS BODY.

HEARING HIS ROARS AS HE FELL, MURA'S SEVEN SONS CAME RUSHING OUT WITH MACES, SWORDS AND CLUBS.

BUT KRISHNA ROUTED THEM IN NO TIME.

ENOUGH! I HAVE PERMITTED ENOUGH CARNAGE. LET US RIDE OUT AND FINISH THAT IMPUDENT YADAVA WHO DARES DISPLEASE ME — THE INVINCIBLE NARAKASURA! FOLLOW ME ON YOUR ELEPHANTS.

MOUNTED ON HIS ELEPHANT AND LEADING HIS HORDES, NARAKASURA THUNDERED TOWARDS THE GATES OF HIS PALACE.

GARUDA FLEW AT THE ELEPHANTS AND ATTACKED THEM WITH BEAK, WING AND CLAW.

THE FRIGHTENED ELEPHANTS TURNED AWAY...

...AND BEGAN RUNNING BACK TOWARDS THE PALACE. NARAKASURA WAS LIVID WITH RAGE.

YOU VILE BIRD! YOU WILL NOT ESCAPE THIS POWERFUL WEAPON OF MINE.

MEANWHILE FOLLOWED BY A YOUNG ASURA, BHOOMI DEVI* CAME TOWARDS KRISHNA WITH ADITI'S EAR-RINGS AND VARUNA'S UMBRELLA.

COME, BHAGADATTA, LET US PRAISE THE LORD AND SEEK HIS PROTECTION.

PLACING THE STOLEN ARTICLES AT HIS FEET, BHOOMI DEVI SANG HYMNS IN PRAISE OF KRISHNA. THEN—

O LORD! THIS IS NARAKA'S SON, BHAGADATTA. HE PLACES HIMSELF AT YOUR FEET. PLEASE PROTECT HIM.

KRISHNA SMILED.

DO NOT FEAR, BHOOMI DEVI. HE SHALL BE INSTALLED ON HIS FATHER'S THRONE. COME, LET US ENTER THE PALACE.

* NARAKASURA'S MOTHER

WHEN KRISHNA ENTERED THE PALACE, THE 16,100 MAIDENS CAPTURED BY NARAKA GREETED HIM.

PROTECT US, O SLAYER OF THE EVIL NARAKA!

LORD KRISHNA, TAKE US WITH YOU, AWAY FROM THIS PLACE!

SO SHALL IT BE.

KRISHNA TURNED TO BHAGADATTA.

HAVE THESE DAMSELS SENT TO DWARAKA, PROPERLY ESCORTED.

KRISHNA THEN INSPECTED NARAKA'S TREASURY.

HAVE ALL THIS WEALTH SENT TO DWARAKA.

NEXT HE WENT TO NARAKA'S STABLES.

THESE FOUR-TUSKED DESCENDANTS OF AIRAVATA SHOULD BE RETURNED TO INDRA.

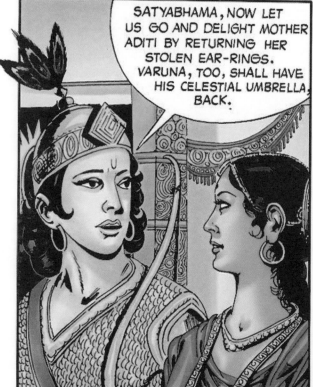

SATYABHAMA, NOW LET US GO AND DELIGHT MOTHER ADITI BY RETURNING HER STOLEN EAR-RINGS. VARUNA, TOO, SHALL HAVE HIS CELESTIAL UMBRELLA BACK.

THEN, MOUNTED ON GARUDA THEY FLEW TOWARDS AMARAVATI TO DELIVER THE STOLEN GOODS.

# KRISHNA AROUND US

**K**rishna is such a beloved character in mythology that stories about him are in abundance. It is out of this love that people include Krishna in regional folklore, resulting in fascinating names and stories for things we see around us.

A short and sweet tale explains the curved shape of a leaf. Krishna was once caught stealing a handful of butter by his mother. He stuffed it into a leaf and rolled it up into a ball to hide it. It is believed that this is why the leaves of this tree have a cup-like shape. The tree is called Ficus Krishnii or the 'Makhan Katori' tree.

In Mahabalipuram, there is a rock that is balanced precariously on a slope, seemingly defying the laws of physics. It is known popularly as 'Krishna's Butter Ball' and 'Vaanirai Kai' in Tamil, which translates to 'Stone of the Sky God.'

In 1908, the then Governor of Madras tried moving the rock because he was afraid it would roll down onto the houses below. He used seven elephants for the task but it did not budge!

# THE SYAMANTAKA GEM

PRINCE SATRAJIT OF DWARAKA WAS A DEVOTEE OF SURYA, THE SUN GOD.

YOUR DEVOTION MERITS A GIFT. THE SYMANTAKA GEM IS YOURS. TAKE IT.

THE SUN GOD DISAPPEARED.

THE JEWEL SHINES SO BRIGHTLY THAT IT LIGHTS MY PATH.

SATRAJIT RODE BACK TO DWARAKA WEARING ABOUT HIM THE RADIANCE OF THE SYAMANTAKA.

WHAT HAS HAPPENED TO OUR PRINCE?

HE SHINES WITH A STRANGE LIGHT.

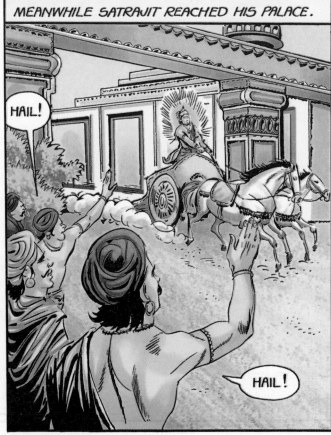

THAT NIGHT HE WENT TO BED, WEARING THE GEM.

THE NEXT MORNING—

GOLD COINS!

HE INSTALLED THE GEM IN A TEMPLE...

...AND WORSHIPPED IT.

IT GIVES FORTH EIGHT MEASURES OF GOLD A DAY!

THE GEM BROUGHT PEACE AND PROSPERITY IN ITS WAKE.

WE HAVE BEEN FAVOURED!

WE WILL NEVER KNOW FAMINE OR WAR!

ONE DAY KRISHNA VISITED SATRAJIT.

WELCOME, SHRI KRISHNA.

DWARAKA IS HUMMING WITH TALES OF YOUR GOOD FORTUNE.

I OWE IT TO SURYA.

BUT IT IS THE FRUIT OF YOUR DEVOTION.

NOW THAT YOU HAVE ENOUGH GOLD, WHY DON'T YOU GIVE THE GEM TO KING UGRASENA?

WHY SHOULD I?

BECAUSE HE IS THE KING. THE GEM WILL BE SAFE WITH HIM.

IT WILL BE EQUALLY SAFE WITH ME. I WILL NOT PART WITH IT.

A FEW DAYS LATER, SATRAJIT'S BROTHER, PRASENA, WENT OUT ON A HUNT, WEARING THE JEWEL.

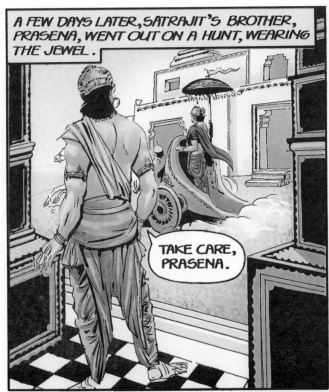

TAKE CARE, PRASENA.

I MAY LOSE MY LIFE BUT I'LL GUARD THE JEWEL.

WHEN HE REACHED THE FOREST, PRASENA DISMOUNTED AND WAITED FOR THE GAME.

AH... AT LAST.

137

A SNAKE!

WHAT A NARROW ESCAPE!

BUT—

AAAGH!

AS THE LION WALKED AWAY WITH THE GEM, JAMBAVAN, KING OF THE BEARS, SAW HIM.

WHAT A FINE JEWEL!

HE ATTACKED THE LION...

...AND KILLED IT.

I'LL GIVE IT TO MY SON.

HERE IS SOMETHING FOR YOU, SON!

MEANWHILE AT DWARAKA —

PRASENA HAS NOT RETURNED FROM THE HUNT.

WHAT COULD HAVE HAPPENED TO HIM?

I AM SURE, KRISHNA MUST HAVE KILLED MY BROTHER FOR THE SAKE OF THE GEM.

SATRAJIT SUSPECTS ME.

I MUST FIND THE JEWEL AND ESTABLISH MY INNOCENCE.

LOOK, GOLD COINS.

THE LION MUST HAVE SOMEHOW GOT HOLD OF THE SYAMANTAKA JEWEL.

AH! THERE LIES OUR CULPRIT.

I WONDER WHO TOOK THE GEM.

DEAD!

I WONDER WHO KILLED IT.

EOOW!

WAA...
WAA...

WHO ARE YOU, STRANGER?

HOW DID YOU GET THE GEM?

THE WINNER TAKES THE GEM.

THEY FIRST FOUGHT WITH WEAPONS.

THEN WITH STONES AND MOUNTAIN ROCKS...

...AND WHEN THOSE WERE EXHAUSTED, WITH UPROOTED TREES.

MEANWHILE, OUTSIDE THE CAVE —

IT IS TWELVE DAYS SINCE HE WENT IN THERE.

HE MUST BE DEAD.

HE ASKED US TO WAIT HERE.

I AM HUNGRY!

I AM TIRED.

LET'S GO HOME.

AN OWL HOOTED ~

WHAT WAS THAT EERIE SOUND?

ONLY AN OWL.

LET'S GO AWAY.

OVERCOME BY FEAR AND EXHAUSTION, THEY LEFT.

MEANWHILE AT DWARAKA KRISHNA'S WIFE AND PARENTS WERE ANXIOUS.

THERE IS NO NEWS OF KRISHNA.

MY LORD, RETURN TO ME, SAFE AND SOUND.

LOOK! A CLOUD OF DUST.

KRISHNA?

BUT—

WE HAVE COME BACK WITHOUT KRISHNA.

WE FEAR HE IS DEAD.

KRISHNA WAS NOT DEAD. AFTER TWENTY EIGHT DAYS OF CONTINUOUS FIGHTING—

YOU ARE INVINCIBLE. I SURRENDER.

ALONG WITH THE GEM PLEASE ACCEPT...

...MY DAUGHTER, JAMBAVATI FOR A WIFE.

I WILL, BUT SOON AFTER THE WEDDING WE MUST RETURN TO DWARAKA. I HAVE TO RESTORE THE GEM TO ITS OWNER.

NO SOONER HAD THEY GARLANDED EACH OTHER THAN JAMBAVATI TURNED INTO A BEAUTIFUL WOMAN.

KRISHNA RETURNED WITH HIS BRIDE AND THE SYAMANTAKA JEWEL TO DWARAKA.

KRISHNA HAS COME, WITH A LOVELY BRIDE.

TELL SATRAJIT TO COME TO THE COURT. I HAVE SOMETHING FOR HIM.

WHEN SATRAJIT CAME—

I HAVE FOUND THE SYAMANTAKA GEM.

AFTER KRISHNA HAD TOLD HIS STORY—

I DID YOU GRIEVOUS WRONG.

IT WAS OUT OF YOUR IGNORANCE.

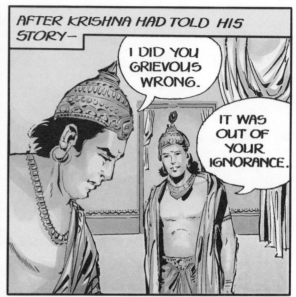

SATRAJIT WANTED TO MAKE AMENDS.

KEEP THE JEWEL, KRISHNA...

...AND ALSO ACCEPT MY DAUGHTER, SATYABHAMA IN MARRIAGE.

I WILL MARRY YOUR DAUGHTER WITH PLEASURE. THE GEM IS RIGHTFULLY YOURS. KEEP IT. YOU MAY HOWEVER GIVE ME THE GOLD IT YIELDS.

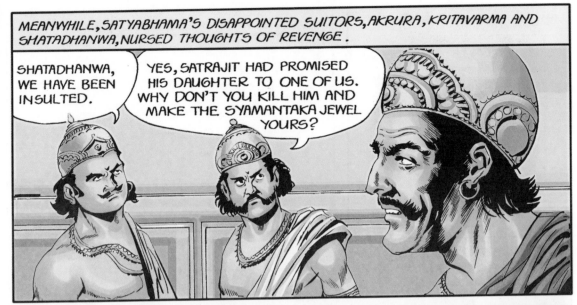

TAKING THE GEM...

...SHATADHANWA RODE AWAY.

THE WOMEN OF SATRAJIT'S HOUSE, SET UP LOUD LAMENTATIONS.

SATYABHAMA WAS HEART-BROKEN.

FATHER...
FATHER...

SHE WENT TO KRISHNA WHO WAS IN HASTINAPURA.

LORD, MY FATHER HAS BEEN SLAIN.

YOU MUST BE BRAVE.

MEANWHILE THE GUILTY SHATADHANWA APPEALED TO KRITAVARMA.

PLEASE, SHELTER ME FROM THE WRATH OF KRISHNA.

GO ELSEWHERE.

SHATADHANWA THEN WENT TO AKRURA WHO GAVE HIM THE SAME ANSWER.

AKRURA, PLEASE KEEP THE GEM WITH YOU THEN. I'M FLEEING FROM DWARAKA.

SHATADHANWA FLED. KRISHNA AND HIS BROTHER, BALARAMA WHO FOLLOWED IN HOT PURSUIT SOON CAUGHT UP WITH HIM.

HALT! YOU MURDERER.

IT'S KRISHNA. I'M DOOMED.

NEAR MITHILA, ONE OF SHATADHANWA'S HORSES TRIPPED...

...AND FELL.

SHATADHANWA FELL DEAD.

HE DOES NOT HAVE THE JEWEL. HE MUST HAVE GIVEN IT TO AKRURA.

WHEN KRITAVARMA LEARNT OF SHATADHANWA'S FATE—

KRISHNA HAS KILLED SHATADHANWA, I HEAR.

HE WILL COME HERE NEXT. LET US FLEE BEFORE HE GETS HERE.

A FEW DAYS LATER AT DWARAKA—

UNLESS THE GEM IS FOUND, I WILL REMAIN SUSPECT IN THE EYES OF THE PEOPLE. ONLY AKRURA CAN HELP ME. I WILL SEND FOR HIM.

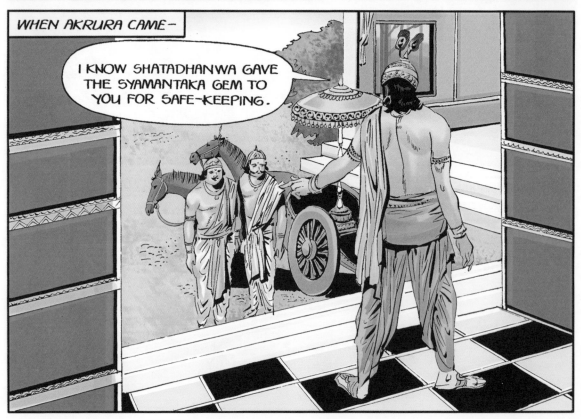

WHEN AKRURA CAME—

I KNOW SHATADHANWA GAVE THE SYAMANTAKA GEM TO YOU FOR SAFE-KEEPING.

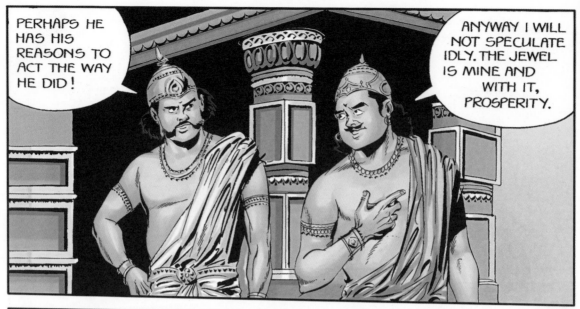

PERHAPS HE HAS HIS REASONS TO ACT THE WAY HE DID!

ANYWAY I WILL NOT SPECULATE IDLY. THE JEWEL IS MINE AND WITH IT, PROSPERITY.

HAVING SET THE MINDS OF THE CITIZENS AT REST KRISHNA TOO WAS ABLE TO RELAX IN THE COMPANY OF HIS HOUSEHOLD.